Kitchen Cupboard Cures

Traditional remedies from the days before you could afford the doctor

Kath Reynolds

To contact the author to purchase further copies of this book or to enquire about talks or reminiscence sessions, please see contact details at the end of the book.

ISBN   978-1-5262-0043-3

Published by Kath Reynolds 2016

Printed by - 4edge Limited, 7a Eldon Way Industrial Estate, Hockley, Essex SS5 4AD

Foreword

This book has been compiled after many, very enjoyable years of reminiscing with the good people of the Midlands, on the theme of "Goose Grease and Brown Paper" – or traditional home remedies for the most common of ailments.

I first became interested in this topic when I was a child and my mother told me to dab butter on a banged head... "How odd!" I thought. As we move through life we have all administered, encountered or been the victim of all sorts of curious remedies for childhood conditions – "put vinegar on it", "keep your liberty bodice on", "eat chicken soup", "don't sit on the garden wall or you'll get chincough" and when all else fails... "Kiss it better".

As a former librarian, I am aware that there are many books about traditional remedies. These range from the very worthy Culpeper's Herbal to the quite inspirational stories shared in "Can we afford the doctor?" published by Age Exchange. Nowadays, there are numerous websites too. My starting point for beginning my "Goose Grease" crusade was talking to older members of my family and then undertaking research through a wide variety of books (a few of which are listed at the end of this book). The remedies described largely relate to the early twentieth century through to the establishment of the NHS...but many are still practiced today.

We must always remember that people didn't "inflict" these homemade cures on their nearest and dearest out of spite or lack of concern but, quite simply, because they either didn't have access to, or couldn't afford to pay for, a doctor. Although it does seem that pre-NHS a good many doctors would happily be paid in garden produce if necessary.

Reminiscence is my great passion. I love to hear the personal stories that history often fails to record. I have delivered interactive sessions to groups both large and small on a wide range of subjects including washdays, schooldays, "waste not, want not", playground games, World War Two...not forgetting courtship and the romantic monkey run! However, Goose Grease and Brown Paper (the session on which this book is based) has always been my favourite session by far- I just can't get enough of the curiosities which people have endured. The science behind these cures is a minor

. concern but I do try to give a layman's explanation of most cures...however, sometimes the "cure" defies explanation!

My reminiscence sessions were originally called "In Sickness and In Health" but both goose grease and brown paper became such regular features that I changed the name to this more catchy title which I still use today when I'm out and about sharing the wise words and wondrous cures of yesteryear. The title could easily have been vinegar and onions, sugar and honey, string on the door or any number of other household combinations.

By the mid-1990's I had co-written and was delivering Open College Network accredited courses training people to work creatively with reminiscence with older people in a variety of settings. I had the great privilege of taking part in the BBC's People's War project in 2005 and had the most amazing stories shared – these can still be found on the BBC People's War website.

Much fun has been had by myself and many others in collecting the snippets of information and colourful stories presented here. I must, however, mention the marvellous ladies of the Women's Institutes and Townswomen's Guilds and the many,

many residential and care settings, not forgetting the church groups, garden guilds and rotary clubs who have invited me along to reminisce with some of the most fascinating folks it has been my privilege to meet. I am indebted to you all but most especially those who tell me their dark secrets, in private, at the end of the session. Thank you!

Before looking at some good, old-fashioned remedies, I would like to ruminate on that great British obsession, second only to discussing the weather, we like to talk about our health and wellbeing. Many of our traditional sayings and nursery rhymes reflect this interest in health...

Phrases and Rhymes of British Culture

Our health and its maintenance is the focus of many of our popular sayings and there is often much truth enshrined within them. Here's a flavour of just a few.

An apple a day keeps the doctor away

One of our most well-loved phrases and one which has more than a grain of truth. Apples are rich in vitamins and fibre, and generally have been widely available in Britain over the years as one of the true home-grown fruits. Nowadays we only have to walk into a supermarket to be regaled with banners and fliers informing us that we must eat five fruit and vegetable portions every day in order to stay fit and well. Apples may well be good for us but it probably wasn't their precise medicinal properties that were being exalted when this phrase was first coined. In olde English the word "apple" was commonly used to describe any round fruit that grew on a tree. Adam and Eve's forbidden fruit, which they ate in the Garden of Eden, is often described as an apple but, in the 1611 King James Version of the Bible, it is just called 'a fruit'.

So where did our modern saying originate? Well, it can certainly be tracked back to 1866 and the *Notes and Queries* magazine which noted a well-used Pembrokeshire proverb -"Eat an apple on going to bed, and you'll keep the doctor from earning his bread."

Early in the 20th century Elizabeth Wright recorded a Devonian dialect version in "Rustic Speech and Folklore" - "Ait a happle avore gwain to bed, An' you'll make the doctor beg his bread"

All good things have their downside though and whilst apples might aid the immune system, reduce cholesterol and protect the brain cells against disorders like Alzheimer's disease, they may also lead to more trips to the dentist. Acids in apples start to rot the enamel on teeth and then the sugars hasten the decay... resulting in the less well-known phrase "An apple a day keeps the dentist in pay"!

Of course there are one or two other sayings connected with fruit and vegetables in our diet... "Eat your greens", "Carrots help you see in the dark"

Vegetables of every colour do us good as they contain vitamins and anti-oxidants which help to reduce the fatty deposits which can cause strokes or heart attacks.

Beans and peas are an easily absorbed source of fibre – so will help to keep you "regular".

Beware too, the onion – if an apple a day will keep the doctor away; then an onion a day will keep your neighbours away!

Coughs and sneezes spread diseases

Coughing and sneezing are the body's quick and natural way of getting rid of germs....but do they leave our body, only to be taken on by some other poor soul?

The advice during the swine and bird flu epidemics was to throw away your tissue immediately after use and to use anti-bacterial handwash. Everyone was armed with little bottles of the solution so they could wash their hands wherever they were. Some folks even went as far as wearing masks when out in public.

However, the saying "coughs and sneezes spread diseases" goes back to the Second World War when the government were keen to make sure that the nation stayed as fit and healthy as possible in order to support the war effort. Posters could be seen dotted around advising everyone to "trap the germs in your handkerchief". No sanitising handwash to carry around then though!

COUGHS and SNEEZES SPREAD DISEASES

COVER UP!

Stop Germs from Spreading

You'll catch your death of cold

Grandma's traditional warning to "dress up warm" against cold or wet weather. I think we identify with this more now when we see teenagers hanging

around on street corners in flimsy tee-shirts and short skirts; not a coat in sight. And don't even think about a woolly vest or a liberty bodice!

Many infectious diseases like the common cold are cyclical with the seasons, though generally we seldom understand why.

Never mind, there's always the flu jab!

Cold hands, warm heart

I always share this adage as the rhyme of the courting couple, as the young gentleman would reassure his lady friend that the reason his hands were so cold was because his heart was so focused on his love for her, it hadn't the strength to warm the rest of his body!

In fact, there may be quite a bit of truth in this one. I was somewhat taken aback when visiting a rotary club to be told that one of the group was a consultant cardiologist. Malcolm was the loveliest chap and patiently explained and confirmed that, yes, this saying may well be true for the body if not for the soul! When under threat from a cold (or other ailments), in order to protect the internal organs most especially the heart, the body closes down the non-essentials, like fingers and toes. Goosebumps are our body's attempt at insulation, followed by shivering to generate warmth through muscle movement. Thanks Malcolm!

I've not repeated quite so often the moving story shared by Doug. Doug confessed that he would suggest to his girlfriend how she might warm her hands on those cold winter evenings of post-war Britain! It involved putting her hand in his pocket and not his coat pocket! I will leave the rest to your imagination... Not one for the faint hearted.

Fish is good for the brain

Well eating fish won't make you a genius overnight,

 but it certainly helps keep the brain and the nervous system in good working order. Especially the oily fish like mackerel and herring which help protect the brain from strokes. Rich in Omega 3, oily fish helps to keep the arteries clear but is also an excellent source of vitamins A and D which help the eyesight and build strong bones. Interestingly, oily fish is also now being recommended for sufferers of chronic fatigue syndrome.

Feed a cold, starve a fever

There is lots of truth in this saying. We all know that when we are poorly we have to keep up our strength by eating. Simply putting hot food, especially proteins, in to the body helps to fight infection and viruses. Granny would always tell you that you should have chicken soup if you weren't well. Why? Well some research in Nebraska has begun to prove that Granny wasn't wrong.

50% MORE CHICKEN

Hot chicken soup has been proven to reduce inflammation and stop runny noses much more effectively than plain old vegetable soup. The esteemed University boffins are still trying to find out why though. Our local doctor tells me that in chicken soup we have the mix of fats and spices in the broth which has a particularly soothing effect on colds and congestion. Sounds about right!

Cast ne'r a clout 'til May be out

Can the vest, liberty bodice or Thermogene waistcoat be taken off yet?

Over the years I've had lots of fun with this one... are we referring to May the month or May the blossom? The consensus of the groups I've talked with seems to be that with climate change the two have probably collided, so the point is moot! However, it is interesting to look at how we came to have the two points of view.

The "'til May be out" part is where the doubt lies. On the face of it this means 'until the month of May is ended'.

There is, however, another interpretation. In England, during May you can't miss the hawthorn blossom. It is an extremely common tree in the English countryside, especially in hedgerows. Hawthorn is virtually synonymous with hedgerows. The tree gives its beautiful display of flowers in late April/early May. It is known as the May Tree and the blossom itself is called May. Using that allusion, 'till May is out' could mean, until the hawthorn is out of bloom.

My personal feeling, and that of most of my reminiscers, is that it is in fact the blossom we are talking about. No one is ever in any doubt about the word "clout" though – a lovely old slang word which can be traced back to at least the 15th Century. Used not only for an item of clothing but also for a quick smack around the head!

Eat your crusts – they will make your hair curl

More of a "waste not, want not" caution, than an aid to curly hair. This saying harks back to pre-Victorian times when food was in short supply and crusts on bread were so hard they were often wasted. Back then curly hair was very desirable so young and old alike were encouraged to eat their crusts to be in fashion and to reduce waste. It probably wouldn't hoodwink anyone nowadays as modern hairdressing could sort that out for you in a couple of hours and not a crust in sight! It would be cheaper to eat your crusts though!

Lick your wounds / Kiss it better

Two sayings used in different contexts but both extolling the healing virtues of our own saliva. How often in childhood days did our mothers sympathise with our bumps and scrapes by offering to kiss the wounded area better? Equally often we would have heard the phrase "He's gone off to lick his wounds" when there had been a falling out or a telling off.

The healing power of saliva, but more especially the saliva of our pets, is perhaps not socially acceptable but it is, all the same, considered quite effective. Saliva is part of our immune system; it obviously contains large amounts of water (ideal for cleansing wounds), but more importantly, the proteins and enzymes in our saliva are anti-bacterial. There are several historical stories of injured masters being saved by the fanatical "licking of their wounds" by their faithful hounds. The thought of choosing this as the first option is not quite so appealing to us today.

Nursery Rhymes

Of course our health obsession also extends to our traditional nursery rhymes. Many rhymes have a health and well-being origin, although on occasion some may be a little tenuous. Sadly a lot of rhymes are now falling out of use, but those of us who grew up with the old favourites like "Oranges and Lemons" and "Humpty Dumpty" will never forget them. We may not have been so keen had we been aware of the history or true meaning of many of the rhymes. Most of the older generation will be able to quickly recall at least half a dozen nursery rhymes and amongst them will be a personal favourite. Not so the children of today, but that's a sad tale for another day. Here are some health related curiosities of our rhyming past...

Did you know that Little Miss Muffet was written about Dr Thomas Muffet who, as well as being a medical doctor, was an insect expert? The "Little Miss" is believed to be his daughter Patience who would have whiled away the hours sitting on a tuffet only to be disturbed by one of her father's wretched spiders.

The history of Oranges and Lemons and the ending "chop off your head" has various interpretations. Bells were often used to inform all of what was happening, as indeed church bells do to some extent today. In the 16th century, those about to be executed were paraded around London to the tolling of the bells...this dubious honour may even have been extended to include the unfortunate wives of Henry VIII. Another version is that chopping off your head referred to young ladies losing their virtue. Whichever one you choose it's going to have quite an impact on your general well-being!

Most of us grew up understanding that "Ring-a-roses" was the rhyme that little children were singing as plague sufferers lay a-moaning and a-groaning on their death beds. We knew that when these poor  folks said "Atishoo" they were very unlikely to get up again. We knew, too, that their "pocket full of posies" was a rich pomander of magical herbs to protect them from the prevailing germs. The mix of herbs might include rosemary, thyme, cloves, cinnamon and nutmeg mixed with a bit of onion....oh and a dash of grated unicorn horn would help too! Have you ever seen a unicorn? No? You may need to come and hear my talk to discover why you've not seen one...

The belief that children were singing "Ring-a-roses" in the 1660's has now been dashed by many historical commentators who say that it was in fact a recollection of the times of the plague, and not a ditty sung during the epidemic. Shame!

On the subject of posies, Barbara, a very charming former mayor, prompted me that, at the start of court sessions, judges would traditionally carry a pomander of herbs. A bit of research reveals that this tradition goes back to the Old Bailey in 1750. Prisoners from Newgate Prison were brought in to court in a very unwashed and pungent condition. Within a short space of time, the judges and several of the dignitaries died of "jail fever". To counter the smells and germs of prisoners in summer months, judges took to carrying their own posy of sweet smelling garden flowers and having the dais and dock areas sprinkled with aromatic herbs. No judge has ever died of jail fever whilst carrying a posy! The posy might also be known by the rather wonderful term "tuzzy muzzy" which can be traced back to the fifteenth century.

We get back in to the realm of curing ailments again when we encounter lovely old Jack and Jill as  they wander up that famous hill – a hill which, according to a much travelled lady from Pelsall, can be found in a Somerset village where most of the population bear the surname Gilson (or Jill's son!!). I'm sure everyone recalls that Jack did in fact mend his broken head with a drop of vinegar smeared on brown paper and plastered upon his forehead. I think I'd opt for my Grandma's drop of cologne on her hankie but that's personal preference! Ah, good old 4711.

All these ditties and sayings bring us to the real business of the day and how are we to set about curing our most common ailments when there's not enough money to pay the doctor? Cures were often effected simply by using items found in every household, sometimes extending out to the garden and occasionally beyond the garden gate too, but always bearing in mind the advice of Hippocrates, who said:

"Let your food be your medicine and your medicine be your food"

Hippocrates, considered to be the father of modern medicine, lived in 4th Century Greece (the modern day party island of Kos, to be precise).Hippocrates was the first to advocate a healthy diet as being instrumental to maintain a strong, fit body and mind. A note of caution, Hippocrates also advocated some serious action with swords -"Extreme remedies are very appropriate for extreme diseases. What medicines do not heal, the lance will; what the lance does not heal, fire will." Hope that's not in the Hippocratic Oath!

Before reading on, I do need to add a further note of caution, please **don't try these at home**!

I don't want to be held responsible for any perforated ear drums, upset tummies or loss of life...

So how would you cure a...

Sore Throat

The sore throat, that most common of ailments – whether it is a minor irritation or verging on quinsy - nearly everyone I've met has chirped up with "honey and lemon" as their first choice remedy. Honey, mildly antibiotic as well as soothing, mixed

 with the acidity of the lemon will help to reduce any infection. Some good old-fashioned vitamin C from the lemon won't go amiss either. How do we

mix the two together? Any way you like but commonly with a drop of hot water or maybe some warm lemonade....but almost always with a good dollop of whisky! Even the most righteous confess

to having whisky in the house purely for medicinal purposes only, you understand! Moorlands folk advise that the ratio of whisky to honey and lemon is crucial - it should be three parts whisky to one part honey and lemon!

Honey, especially Manuka honey, is now being used worldwide in the fight against infection. Mildly antibiotic and antibacterial, around the world pure honey is used to treat everything from sore throats to burns and bedsores. For your sore throat remedy, you may want to try substituting the honey with some lovely gloopy glycerine.

Gargles - who has not been encouraged to gargle with salt water to quell that nasty throat? Ugh, it's ok so long as you remember not to swallow! Salt is recognised everywhere for its sterilising and cleansing powers. Used as a preservative for centuries, salt also conquers minor infections. The more adventurous might choose to gargle with salt and vinegar or even vinegar and sugar but almost everyone will have experienced the burning sensation of a TCP gargle. My good friend Judy recommends gargling with alcohol – but always remember that you **must** swallow with this one! Caribbean elders tell me that they would gargle with a sage infusion – but not made with green sage, it must be red sage. Other gargles would include a peroxide solution and some of that household favourite, Bicarbonate of Soda. Apparently slowly drinking the bicarb solution works wonders in many ways and not just curing your poorly throat...more of that later!

Not one for the ladies, but a sweaty sock tied round the throat will ease any soreness. A source from North Carolina in 1910 reckoned that the dirtier the sock, the more rapid the cure -*"If you have a sore throat, take the stocking you have been wearing and tie it around your neck. Some say the dirtier the stocking is, the better."* I think I'd go for the more civilised, freshly laundered lisle stocking or, better yet, the luxurious silk scarf tied around my neck! However, the sweaty sock does have multiple uses; you can use it to polish up your shoes afterwards.

Personally I favour many of the civilised remedies including ice cream and chocolate. Chocolate? Just think on that lovely cube of choc dissolving in to a gorgeous gooey mess on your tongue. When consumed, it will kiss your throat with its chocolaty richness and so aid restful swallowing. Perfect!

Grandma's remedies were always tried and trusted but quite often the phrase "kill or cure" also springs to mind. Several years ago a lady shared with me the story of her little boy who was very poorly one Christmas Eve back in the 1940's; his throat was closing and the infection in it was causing him to feel very ill. Grandma arrived... and Grandma asked mum if she had "a piece of fatty bacon and a piece of string". Being Christmas Eve and the goose awaiting its fate, both bacon and string were ready to hand. Grandma tied the bacon and string together and forced the poorly lad to swallow the raw fatty bacon; a few seconds later Grandma pulled on the string and withdrew the bacon from his throat! The lad wasn't 100% on Christmas Day but he was at the very least 50% better. Who knows what caused this miraculous recovery? Was it the greasy bacon coating and easing his throat, was it the saltiness of the bacon sterilising the throat or was it the fear that Grandma might inflict this torture again? I'm sure I would have said that I felt better too...just in case Grandma re-applied the treatment!

Sulphur was one of the remedies available from the chemist and several people have told me they had  sulphur powder blown on to their tonsils in an attempt to sterilise any infection. One lady rather sheepishly told me the story of her mother's sore throat remedy - Mother would toddle off to Dad's pigeon shed, pluck a feather from a dozing pigeon and return to her ailing child. She would then dip the feathery ends in to sulphur powder and proceed to paint her poor child's throat with the tickly, somewhat grubby, pigeon feather...does the phrase "kill or cure" spring to mind again?

Whilst you've got the pigeon feather to hand, you could try painting the throat with gentian violet. Others suggest that rather than gentian violet, you should boil up a pan of violet leaves to make another wondrous gargle.

Apparently a bit of chlorate of potash would have done the trick years ago too. Not now though, it's been taken off the market – it seems it was highly explosive! I love to share the wartime story of the two sisters who charmingly pushed chlorate of potash pellets in to the ends of their soldier brother's cigarettes, as he slumbered in front of the fire whilst home on leave from the Front. On waking up the lad reached for his cigarettes, lit one and the flare promptly relieved him of his eyebrows and lashes!

Teas, or infusions, were highly recommended for sore throats- either as a soothing drink or a gargle. Thyme tea, raspberry leaf tea, blackcurrant tea, ginger tea.

As a last resort, you could hark back to the middle ages and try the friendly frog in your throat remedy. Ugh, literally!

Chesty Cough

So many poorly coughs have been tended by a range of home-grown remedies. Unsurprisingly, the remedies range from the soothing to the torturous.

At the top of my list for curing those chesty conditions would be some good, solid onion remedies. Onions as part of the allium family have powerful anti-bacterial and antiseptic qualities...remember those Ring-a-roses kiddies with their magical herbal mix all blended together with a juicy onion?

There are many stories from the twentieth century flu epidemics of people warding off colds and flu by simply keeping chopped onions in their bedrooms. The theory being that the onion absorbs any bacteria in the atmosphere thus protecting the sleeping humans!

In 1919, the flu epidemic killed 40 million people worldwide. A local doctor visited a farm where everyone was fit and healthy. When the doctor asked what they were doing that was different, the farmer's wife replied that every night she had placed a peeled, chopped onion in a dish in their bedrooms. Any infected air which was exhaled during the night was absorbed by the selfless onion. Nowadays we are advised never to leave half an onion uncovered to use the next day. By the time the next day comes, the onion will have been soaking up the germs and bacteria all around it and be unfit for use. I imagine every one of us has used a chopped onion to counteract the fumes and smells of gloss paint? Same principle. Interestingly a discussion with a group of farmers revealed that during the "Foot and Mouth" epidemics they too had used chopped onions to protect their animals from that vicious disease. They claimed it was very effective.

Onions combined with sugar will also form an effective cure for chesty conditions. A roughly chopped onion liberally sprinkled with brown sugar, would be left to stand until all the juices drained from the onion and combined with the sugar to form a soothing linctus. Sugar, like the honey mentioned earlier, has the same antibiotic and antibacterial qualities, especially in its purest forms. Curiously, a group of Asian ladies have told me of a very similar cure where they would use a turnip in place of the onion. A Romanian colleague agreed that she had also experienced sugar being used to draw the juices from a vegetable to treat a bad chest but her experience was with a radish. Not one of our puny little red radishes, but one of the elongated white radishes (mooli) found especially in Eastern Europe. It would be hollowed out and sprinkled with sugar and the juices swallowed to soothe the chest in the same way.

Another sugary remedy was administered to the chesty children of mining communities. Pitmen would take a slice of bread and butter liberally sprinkled with sugar down the pit with them. During the course of their shift they would leave the "sugar sandwich" exposed to the coal dust and pit air. Seemingly it worked a treat when fed to the ailing child!

Many families would have their own secret blend of cough linctus prepared with years of love and experience by mum or grandma and using mainly natural ingredients. Berries would feature very strongly in these mixtures. Children would be sent out to forage the hedgerows for blackberries, bilberries, blackcurrants, etc. not just to make a pie for Sunday tea, but also to get the berries for the cough mixture brewing for the winter months. The currants and berries would be boiled with combinations of sugar, honey or vinegar and the resulting compound would be stored on the top shelf of the pantry until the first coughs and splutters of the winter months appeared. A fabulous personal recipe/remedy book belonging to a Miss Hill of Stone and written around the turn of the 20th Century was shared with me a few years ago, and has now become one of my most treasured possessions. This book lists many recipes and remedies. It includes the Hill family cough linctus recipe which contains "six quarts of blackberries"-the fruit should be "ripe but sound".

One of my own personal favourites would be the delicious raspberry vinegar and olive oil. That elegant bottle with the two liquids completely separated and having to be vigorously shaken to re-blend them together. The sickly taste and slimy texture as it slithered down the throat was quite unlike any other. Some folks say that their mothers would have made their own version of this remedy and would often substitute blackberry vinegar. Presumably these fruits were more readily available.

Of course, goose grease and brown paper might very well make an appearance when curing chesty conditions – most families were strong believers in the poultice. It may have been plastered with goose

grease but it could equally have been mustard and lard, kaolin, camphor, Friar's Balsam, bread, etc. The various compounds would be heated and secured to the chest occasionally with brown paper and a bit of muslin or lint, but most often with a nice piece of red flannel. It had to be red flannel, no other colour would do. For centuries, red has been regarded as the colour of healing. During the plague, rich people would lie in beds made up with red covers and even surround themselves with red ornaments in order to ward off the evil germs. My own Grandma wore a red flannel waistcoat all her life after contracting scarlet fever as a girl; her belief being that the red flannel would protect her from succumbing to further illness.

Of course a lovely Thermogene vest or waistcoat would have had a reddish tone too. Impregnated with the chemical equivalent of chillies and peppers, the pinkish red hues of Thermogene would have brought much comfort to many.

Red, we all perceive to be a rich, warm colour but could there be any other reason why red was always used for a poultice? I surfed the internet for hours and only found people as perplexed as myself. A kindly chap who had been a colour chemist, enlightened me by explaining how the colours on the colour spectrum have differing abilities to absorb and retain or reflect heat; red is up there with the dark colours as one of the best heat retainers. Well, if it's good enough for Santa Claus...

A very touching story was shared by a lovely lady who told me how her baby daughter was suffering with pneumonia in the 1940's. The doctor visited every day for a fortnight and gave the little girl a series of nasty injections. After two weeks, it still seemed to be having no effect and the doctor advised that that night could go either way for the little mite. The family were desperate. They decided to try something recommended by an elderly neighbour and gave their baby a teaspoon of glycerine. Once the baby had swallowed the glycerine, she was held upside down by her feet and her back gently rubbed until she started to vomit. A worrying night was spent watching the little lass as she wretched but she did make a complete recovery. Was it the doctor's mysterious injections or was it the teaspoon of glycerine? Her mum was convinced that it was the sainted glycerine!

The steam bath was, and still is today, one of the best known and most common cures for that blocked up feeling. Some may have had a special

steam kettle but for most it would have been a lovely big bowl of steaming hot water and a nice white towel (yes, it had to be white!) In to the boiling water would go a generous dollop of any number substances ranging from Vick to Friar's Balsam, eucalyptus to Olbas oil. Menthol crystals would have also been well used and to my mind these little pin heads of dynamite could easily be mistaken for primitive chemical warfare! Anyone who has exceeded the dosage of the tiny menthol flakes, will have probably also experienced the scary sensation of their breath being taken away and blurred vision for the rest of the day.

Inhaling strong smells was widely acknowledged to help dislodge any blockages in your tubes. It may have been a sweet little camphor bag pinned to your vest. Or, when the occasion demanded, many people would have been advised to dress up warmly and then go out to where new roads were being laid and "sniff the tar". Tar is wonderfully potent when inhaled and this was particularly recommended for children suffering from whooping cough. However, if there weren't any new roads about, you could always nip along to the gas works and have a good sniff or ask a friendly farmer if you could stand in his cow shed and inhale the fumes of the cow muck! Both are just as effective it seems.

You might choose to administer Vick in a variety of ways other than in the steam bath - but how many would rub it in to their feet to ease a chesty cough? Whilst we are pondering on feet, you may want to fill a bowl with hot water and add a generous dollop of mustard...then soak your feet to ease your cold symptoms. Whilst you're soaking your feet, if the mustard doesn't work for you, then try a potash solution.

Swallowing a generous spoonful of black treacle would be beneficial to sufferers of chesty complaints. Sounds lovely and sweet but the molasses would be most effective when combined with yet more sugar, mustard or vinegar...Yuk! Add some sulphur to the mix and we have the magical brimstone and treacle.

If that cough was to turn seriously nasty and whopping cough developed, then the following, peculiar course of action may be taken:

"If your child has whooping cough, pass him under a donkey's belly, or take him for a donkey ride along

the seafront. If that fails, place him before the fire and rub his feet liberally with hog's lard or goose grease. Then give him four live woodlice in a spoonful of jam or treacle, and the 'whoop' will vanish. Or, catch and skin a field mouse, make a small pie for your child to eat, and strap the skin of the mouse to his throat – furry side down – for nine days".

Another one not for the feint hearted, go out at dawn and collect the liquid from a day old cowpat. Don't worry, you only need to drink a teaspoonful!

Now I know where they got the ideas from on the reality TV show "I'm a celebrity, get me out of here!"

Whilst visiting a rural WI, I was advised that the best cure for a bad chest is to have your chest rubbed by a strange man. Naturally I sought clarification of whether this should be strange as in someone I didn't know, or strange as in a bit odd. The considered advice was if you can find someone who is a bit of both, then that'll be all to the good!

If all else fails, you could resort to another of Doug's remedies and rub your chest with half a brick!

Boils

We don't hear much about boils nowadays but, in years gone by, suffering with boils was very common. People with diabetes and similar conditions would be very susceptible but so would many a young lad whose starched shirt collar would be a major irritation to those unsightly boils.

Creating a drawing ointment and putting it on to a poultice would be an excellent starting point. Sugar and soap would be the most effective, but, as I was cautioned by one lady, it should always be carbolic

soap. However, several other people have assured me that green household soap will work equally well. Sugar is known by many folk healers for having unique properties to draw at the same time as being mildly antiseptic. The sugar and soap preparation should be applied and left for as long as possible to draw out the boil. Or, as I like to say, left to fester!

Applying toothpaste to a boil will help to draw it, as will mustard plasters or an application of Epsom Salts or Fullers Earth. However, the late Dr McDermott recommended an application of fresh cow muck to shift those stubborn boils. The lady who shared this little gem said she couldn't say if it worked or not as she most definitely did not try it! Readers should note that further investigation has revealed that, in order for the cow muck remedy to be effective, you must personally scare the cow in to delivering the required excrement and use it immediately!

This next story that stands in my memory as the goriest was told to me by Joan who had been brought up in a Staffordshire village and, when she was aged 7, she had a nasty boil on her eyelid. It was very painful and poor Joan couldn't open her eye -then Grandma arrived. Grandma told Joan's mother to fetch a clean, empty milk bottle and to put the kettle on. The bottle was filled with boiling water and then quickly emptied to create a vacuum. The bottle was swiftly placed over the boil on Joan's eyelid and the vacuum drew out the offending boil. Painful? It was indeed! Joan said she could still hear the pop of the boil bursting in to the bottle 70 years later!

"Squeeze it!" would be the chant of many, but my Dad would say that a "karate chop" might also work. My Dad attended a grammar school in the North East of England in the days when discipline reigned supreme. On one occasion he failed to halt in the corridor when the loathed Maths teacher was passing. The Maths teacher took the side of his hand to the back of Dad's neck and yelled "Out of my way, boy!" The smile was on my Dad's face and not the beloved Master's, when the boil on Dad's neck popped into teacher's hand!

Warts

Years ago it was not uncommon for people to be plagued by lots of unsightly warts. They would be willing to try any remedy in order to dispense with the horrible things.

The first thought for most people would be "rub it with a piece of steak and bury the steak in the garden". This was indeed a well-used cure but there are various elements to the cure that simply rubbing and burying the steak don't take into account. First of all, you should steal the steak – preferably from your neighbour but, if they're not rich enough to afford steak, then steal from anyone. You must rub the wart with the steak, then take the steak and bury it. Don't bury it in the garden though – it needs to be buried at the crossroads. All of this should be undertaken under the cover of darkness and the steak should be buried at midnight. Then, as the buried steak rots in the ground, so will your wart begin to wither and disappear. However, you must not tell anyone or the cure simply won't work.

You could also try rubbing the inside of a broad bean pod or a banana skin on the wart. The broad bean pod should not be buried though. It needs to be flung carelessly over your shoulder. You must not be tempted to look back to check where it has landed; you must walk away and leave it where it has fallen. As the pod rots away and dies... so will your wart disappear.

It seems that mud is good for "drying out" warts. The stories shared by Ivy who had been born and bred in Southend had me picturing a comical sight. The mud on the beaches of Southend is apparently highly recommended for treating warts. Ivy said that as a child she would often go down to the Southend beach to find hordes of people bathing in the mud. No more trekking to Turkey for your mud bath, just nip along to Southend for some superior quality mud!

Many people have told me about slugs and snails and how effective their "goo" is for drying up warts.

Simply allow the slug or snail to sit upon the wart for a short while and excrete its goo. Then you must take the snail and impale it upon a hawthorn. As the snail withers and dies (you've guessed it) so the wart will disappear!

Cures for multiple warts include dropping the corresponding number of safety pins down the lavatory and waiting until they go rusty in the bottom of the pan - by this time your warts will have disappeared. All of the remedies discussed so far have one thing in common and that is time. We now know that warts are viral and will go in their own good time!

Your fasting spittle will also be effective in drying out the wart. You should "nibble" or lick the wart immediately after you wake up in the morning and the acidity in the mouth will start to reduce the wart day by day. Dabbing with urine or aromatic vinegar will also work.

Regular dabs of milk thistle will help to dry out warts. Where would you find a ready-made, natural supply

of milk thistle? If you trawl back to your childhood days and gathering wildflowers, you may recall getting your fingers covered in a gooey sap when you picked a dandelion? That goo in the stem of the dandelion is milk thistle.

Of course picking dandelions comes at a risk. Would you want to wee the bed?

Sulphur can also be used to treat a wart. People would generally lick an old fashioned red top match and then rub the match-head over the wart. The sulphur will draw and dry the wart. A few brave souls would strike the match, blow it out and cauterise the wart! Some people used simple remedies like rubbing with a caustic pencil or salt, but weird and wonderful cures are, of course, much more interesting.

Many people have suggested tying a piece of cotton (thread) around the wart to cut off the blood supply. This works well but is much better if you can find a piece of horsehair to tie around instead. Anne told me how her mother would tell her to run out to the milkman's horse and whip a hair from its tail! Horsehair or cat gut would be much more effective in getting rid of that irksome wart than any piece of cotton.

Ever heard of buying a wart? Warts can be "bought" from the afflicted person but beware, should you actually physically exchange money from one hand to another, then you, the purchaser, will become the afflicted!

Charming a wart is a much more curious cure. Over the years lots of folks have shared stories about whispering and chanting over a wart to get rid of it. But no story has been more fascinating than when the lovely ladies of Coven in South Staffs, shared that of the lady in their village who was famed for charming away warts. I'm very fond of mispronouncing the word Coven (normal pronunciation Co-ven, my mischievous pronunciation is Cu-ven) - you will see why as you read this story...

This "charming" lady in Coven cured many, many people over many, many years and the story goes that some people would only have to step over the threshold of the lady's house for the curing to begin. However, the charming would only work for those who believed in the cure. Ye of little faith wouldn't stand a chance! This lady was acknowledged locally as a

witch (a good witch of course) and lived where the witch always lives...in the last house in the village!

A lady from a rural town, told me that her Granny had charmed away warts when she was a young girl and living in Ireland. The charming always worked. She was very taken by the whole experience so when her own children got warts, she tried to charm them in the same way. All to no effect I'm afraid! A similar tale was shared by someone who told me that their mum was the village charmer and was very successful with everyone's warts except her own daughter who resolutely did not believe in her mum's charming abilities.

To date I have heard of only three male wart charmers...and one of those claimed to be a descendant of the celebrated Molly Leigh, a notorious 18th Century witch!

I think I'd rather pop to the chemist and get some Compound W – guaranteed to banish those ugly warts in a fortnight!

Earache

Earache can be terrible, but, if the problem is of a waxy nature, the remedies are in plentiful supply.

Olive oil would be the first resort of almost everyone I've talked to. Obviously in days gone by there wouldn't have been shelf upon shelf of varying types of olive oil in the local supermarket; you would have to trundle off to the chemists to purchase a small bottle of olive oil. The oil would be warmed and gently poured in to the aching ear. Warming the oil wasn't without its perils – especially if your mother was one of the ones who warmed it over a candle and then burnt your ear with the hot spoon as she poured it into your "lughole"! Once the oil was in the ear it would be secured with a generous blob of cotton wool. My own doctor advised me some years ago that this was not the correct way to use the cotton wool. It should be "twizzled" to a point and then gently inserted in to the ear. That way when the cotton wool was withdrawn, it removed the offending earwax at the same time.

Would you have used a different liquid to loosen the earwax? My mother would always use Almond Oil. Whenever I have shared this fact at sessions I have often been met with bemusement – except from the folks who have originated from the North-East of England. It seems the canny lads and lasses of Geordie-land would have smelled a lot sweeter than other earache sufferers as they sported the delicate perfume of the almond rather than the olive. Other people have confessed to using warmed glycerine in place of olive oil.

Some wouldn't put the oil in their ear at all. Instead they would massage the oil around the back of the ear. The act of massaging would help to loosen the trapped wax. I've been told that Vick will work well with a massage too.

It's interesting to note that doctors are now encouraging people to soften earwax with olive oil in preference to any of the over-the-counter potions available at the chemist. The theory now being that the chemical compounds are too brutal and abrasive and actually dry out the earwax so much that it can become more difficult to remove instead of less.

"My mother would blow cigarette smoke in our ears if we had earache!" The chap who shared this little gem had me lost for words. On further investigation it sounded pretty much like one of the traditional Chinese remedies, the Hopi Ear Candle, so I began to recount this "remedy" in my reminiscence sessions. I was surprised to find that several people had also heard of this curious cure. One lady stopped me in my tracks yet again when she said "It works much better with cigar smoke". It seems her mother had lit up a cigar and puffed the smoke in to the ears of her suffering children! The smoke, much like steam, would find a way through the blockage in the ear and loosen the wax for easier removal.

"Mother used to put peroxide in our ears as youngsters!" Another show-stopper! When Bill shared this sordid secret, I was aghast and asked him if he was sure. "Certain" he replied. I almost hesitated to ask if it worked but he assured me that it was very effective, even if a little like the hubble-bubble of the witch's cauldron as the peroxide fizzed, popped and crackled as it acted upon the wax! I remained unsure about this one until I was talking with a WI one evening and a retired pharmacist chipped in with "Have you not read the ingredients of your bottle of Earex?" It seems that the over the counter remedies are based on a peroxide blend. So, not the stuff you dye your hair with and definitely not neat peroxide, but a peroxide solution. Caution those who do try neat peroxide. One lady told me that her husband had had this cure inflicted upon him as a child. The peroxide not only perforated his eardrum but left him with persistent ear problems to this day. Always read the label!

Heat would be a favoured cure for all manner of ailments; lying your head on a lovely hot water bottle would soothe the nastiest of earaches. What if you didn't have a hot water bottle? A nice hot brick (the sort you would have used to warm your bed) would make a good, if uncomfortable, substitute.

Better still would be the hot oven shelf taken directly from the range or back-to-back oven.

A warmed salt bag would be another reliable source of heat, as would a piece of hot toast. My favourite heat cure though would have to be boiling either an onion or a potato until it was piping hot all the way through, then cutting it in half and dropping the two halves in to an old sock. The sock would then be tied attractively around your head, making sure to fix the onion halves over the ears! Or you might just try taking the hot centre clove from the onion and popping that into your ear. Remember the tales of the onion drawing out flu infection?

Still with the allium family, reminiscing with the Asian community revealed that they would place a warmed garlic clove in the ear in much the same way as the onion clove. Just as effective and not as much waste!

Toothache

If you can't afford the doctor, then it's a fair bet that you won't be able to afford the dentist! Many families would resort to their own, creative methods of dental pain relief.

First off the shelf would be good old oil of cloves. No matter which continent you were born in, cloves or oil of cloves would be the number one home cure for toothache. Some folks might also stretch to a drop of tincture of myrrh. The oil of cloves and tincture of myrrh would be rubbed in to the gums or dabbed on to cotton wool and placed over the throbbing tooth. The actual clove would be bitten down on to release the oils and soothe the pain.

Most households would have in their store cupboard a bottle of medicinal whisky. Whisky dabbed on the offending tooth or gum, whisky dropped in to the gaping tooth cavity or cotton wool soaked in whisky – all have been used to ease that terrible pain. As an absolute last resort, the advice would be "just knock it back!"

A very sweet story was shared with me by Dorothy who said that whenever she had toothache as a child her mother would make a twist out of newspaper and fill it with a mixture of salt and pepper. Every time a twinge of pain was experienced, she would dip her finger into the salt and pepper mixture then rub it on to her gums. The salt would be antiseptic and antibacterial and the pepper would bring the comfort of heat. Sweeter still (or so I thought) at bedtime her mother would tie the paper twist to the wooden bedstead so, as the pain surged during the night, Dorothy would be able to carry on rubbing the mixture in to her gums. How lovely I thought, "I can just see you under your fluffy pink eiderdown, cuddling your teddy and soothing your pain". "Hmm" said Dorothy, "not so good if you were the middle one in the bed and had to reach over a couple of others to get to your dip!" My rosy image was quickly shattered.

Heat would again be a very comforting treatment but once we reached the 1950's with the advent of refrigerators and the growing popularity of frozen foods; cold compresses, most commonly bags of frozen peas, became just as popular.

Some odd remedies have also been shared over the years. Chew bread, chew sesame seeds, rub your gums with pipe tobacco... but perhaps the most curious, keep a peeled potato in your pocket! I'm not sure what possible benefit the peeled potato can have for your tooth but I can all too easily imagine the horrible mess it will make of your pocket!

Of course extreme pain does sometimes call for extreme measures. When the worst came to the worst, many people would resort to the "string on the door" method of extraction! My husband's Grandfather was very proud of the fact that he'd never visited a dentist and had, in fact, extracted his own teeth whenever it had become necessary!

Most would agree that the "string on the door" method would really only be used for baby teeth or teeth which were already loose but others argue that it would be used whatever the circumstances.

I always enjoy sharing my experience of reminiscing with a group of older people and a class of 7 year olds from Jackfield Infants School. We were brought together to celebrate the 75th anniversary of a local hospital. Imagine, if you will, the faces of those 7 year olds as they were regaled with gory stories of manual self-extraction. Horror soon gave way to absolute absorption as the children revelled in the gore! The art work the children produced at the end of our time together was stunning; it largely featured faces, doors and big red splodges in the middle of their piece of paper!

More dramatic still was the story shared by Tom, a former miner. He went on shift one day with a raging toothache. After only a short while underground, the pain became unbearable and he asked to return to the surface. The kindly shotfirer overheard Tom's request and offered to help relieve his pain. Two tiny charges were placed either side of Tom's tooth, then everyone stood back as the charge was detonated. Tom flew across the coal seam and proceeded to knock himself out, but lo and behold the toothache was cured! On visiting a dentist sometime later, Tom was asked where he had had the tooth extracted as "unbelievably" the nerve endings were all dead!

Of course, the fail safe for toothache would always be the tool box and dad's pliers...

Chilblains

Chilblains are one of those complaints that we don't hear too much about any more but they would be the bane of the lives of many folks during the harsh winters of the early and mid-20th century. Chilblains are caused by frozen extremities being warmed up too quickly and the symptoms would include the most unbearable itching and burning sensations. Central heating has probably been the most effective invention to prevent chilblains but there were lots of other remedies too. Two "off the shelf" remedies which were widely used to treat chilblains were Snowfire and Wintergreen ointments.

The most favoured remedy by far for chilblains would be to "put your feet in the chamber pot"! Urine cures are some of the most effective for a range of ailments, but for chilblains the salt in the urine will act as an anti-bacterial and antiseptic agent whilst at the same time the urea will sooth the inflamed skin. Method in their madness? Urea in its basic chemical form is used in all moisturisers...but I don't want you to think that Nivea and Olay are sitting down at the sewage works with their test tubes!

Our good friend the onion comes in useful again to combat chilblains. Dipped in salt, the onion should be rubbed on the feet and the solution allowed to dry. A wonderful aroma!

Boiled parsnip water with a touch of powdered allium allowed to dry on the skin will also work. As will a bit of ginger and mustard to warm the skin.

Standing in fresh snow will soothe the irritation of chilblains too but when all else fails, thrash your feet with holly! I can only imagine that the latter cure will give you something even worse to worry about.

Stye

Colloquially known by the rather inglorious term "powk" in North Staffordshire, a stye would be the most common eye infection that people would contract.

Styes would traditionally be treated with the celebrated Golden Eye ointment; a feature of every medicine cabinet for well over a century. When Golden Eye ointment wasn't available, a compress of cold tea leaves might be applied to the eye, this would be later substituted by a reliable old teabag. Many people say it would be more effective to use a tea poultice, as hot as you could stand it, to draw out the stye. Either way the tannin in the tea helps to draw the infection from the eyelash bed. Many also believe that before applying any solution to the infected area you should first of all pluck out the eyelashes! In doing this the infection can be directly reached with the solution. Borassic powder solutions would also be used by some to soothe the eye.

Our favourite cure for a stye is to rub it with a gold ring. Not some 9 carat, chain store rubbish though; it must be 22 carat gold. The gold rubbed along the eyelid relieves the pressure but it is believed that the stye also responds to the gold.

Remedies from the Asian community include using coriander seeds or onions. Make a solution of one teaspoon of coriander seeds boiled in a cup of water. Use this preparation to wash the eyes 3-4 times a day. Or you could boil an onion (or garlic) and use the boiled water to bathe the eye.

The most curious "cure" for a stye is shared by the ladies of Morley College in London – "place the breast milk of a woman who has borne a baby boy on the affected eyes."

Tummy aches

"Women's troubles" would invariably be treated with a spoonful of Indian Brandy (Brandee) to soothe the cramps of the time of the month. Of course, the trusty hot water bottle would also be called in to action.

Drink a solution of baking powder in hot water, or better still blend together sherbet and lemonade... early versions of liver salts perhaps? A brew made from dried elderflowers will sort your tummy aches. Meg shared a remedy from India. She said that whilst touring the country she had had one or two bugs and been advised that the solution was to drink lemon juice with sugar. Another remedy from my childhood doctor to help build up strength after a tummy bug is to drink fizzy cola with a teaspoon of salt stirred in...it will restore all those electrolytes better than any of those fancy sachets!

Eat burnt toast - charcoal can help with mild digestive upsets, stop diarrhoea, and halt viral and bacterial infections. Charcoal absorbs toxins. The powder can be placed in the mouth and moistened with saliva for swallowing. It is also possible to administer charcoal as a slurry by mixing it with water.

In the days before Nurse Harvey and Woodward's were producing gripe water to soothe our babies, grannies would make a nice drop of cinder tea and administer a teaspoonful to the griped baby.

The active bacteria in yoghurt will soothe stomach infections. Margaret from Trentham was a great believer in the healing power of yoghurt - she would advocate more than just oral ingestion!

Comfrey tea or Slippery Elm would also be used for gastric troubles. Both were in common usage but nowadays are more likely to be used to treat external abrasions.

Mint tea and various other mint combinations will soothe upset stomachs. As will thyme tea, ginger tea or even a drop of ginger wine.

We can't cure every ailment in this little book but, just so you have a few more tricks up your sleeve, here are some random, but intriguing, remedies...

Rheumatism - boil 1/2 pound of chillies in water, then when the water has reduced add in a pint of sweet oil and a half a pint of turpentine. Apply to a poultice of red flannel.

Flatulence - a nice cup of hot clove tea. Or, if you prefer, caraway tea - the fragrance of which is likened to babies gripe water!

Stress and anxiety - Mint tea, a great refresher for when you are "all at sixes and sevens". A wonderful remedy from Miss Hill of Stone. She suggests for "jaded spirits" a drop of rosemary tea. I'm unsure how precise the diagnosis needs to be to justify mint or rosemary tea.

Eczema – Manuka honey, used internally and externally will soothe the irritating itch and soreness.

Diphtheria - sieved lamp oil.

Whitening the skin - a mixture comprising 2oz eau de cologne, 2oz lemon juice and 6oz brown Windsor soap rubbed in to the skin

Nappy rash - Fullers Earth, or raw egg white, or Blue Gentian or liquid paraffin.

Chapped hands – bathe them in fresh urine.

Bumps, bruises and abrasions - cold tea, comfrey leaves or iglodine. Grandmas would frequently keep the cold tea in the teapot when the grandchildren were visiting...just in case there was a mishap and "tea treatment" was needed. Alternatively, bumps could be treated with a cold tablespoon pressed on the affected area. Don't forget the trusty blob of butter rubbed in to reduce swelling and bruising!

Arthritis - vinegar, honey and hot water drunk daily or a teaspoon of coconut oil.

Dressings for wounds - common cottongrass with its fluffy white tops was often collected and used to cover wounds.

Heart problems - digitalis (or foxgloves) would be used to slow and regulate the heartbeat. Digoxin is taken from the plant but it is very poisonous ...prescription only folks!

Gout - sleep with wine bottle corks in your bed...remember to replace them every two months lest they become ineffective! Or drink celery tea.

Toothpaste - fresh soot mixed with salt.

Worms - crushed pumpkin seeds with milk added to make a paste, then washed down with a generous glug of castor oil. Elders of the Caribbean community advised that a refreshing drink of mint tea would normally be on hand to "take the taste away"!

Cholesterol - turmeric infusion drunk daily.

Headaches - "4711" cologne dabbed on the forehead. A traditional Jamaican remedy is to rub bay rum in to a banana leaf and then tie it to your head.

Hair tonic - rosemary infused water...shiny hair and no grey hair.

Chapped lips – another Indian remedy to share - mashed up rose petals made into a balm will soothe.

Insomnia - drink the urine of a prince who has just drunk at least two glasses of wine.

Wrinkles - bathe your face in slug or snail "goo"

Heat Rash – sulphur tablets will cool down your over-heated blood

Prevention is better than cure

Of course the best way to avoid the doctor would be to ensure that you stay fit and well and to this end the phrase "Prevention is better than cure" is the prompt for sharing stories of tonics and toddies administered to ensure robust good health.

Cod liver oil and malt! You either loved it or hated it. Malt would often have kids smacking their lips and asking for more, whereas cod liver oil was more of an acquired taste. I always like to ponder on the children who were dosed up at school. Was a clean spoon used for each child? Unsurprisingly, the overwhelming response is no! Only once has someone volunteered that, as a nursery nurse, she dipped the spoons in hot water before moving to the next child...the rest passed on the germs on the same old spoon!

The brand name of Virol is wistfully whispered as everyone relives the taste combination.

The very distinctive taste of the legendary "Welfare Orange" is remembered with passion and affection. Available on the National Health Service with your welfare tokens; mothers could go along to the "welfare" or clinic to collect a small brown bottle of orange concentrate for their little darlings.

Infinitely preferable (to my mind) to welfare orange juice and its very processed taste, would be the delectable rosehip syrup. The famous brand was Delrosa but some people would collect their own rosehips and produce their own syrup. Rosehip syrup keeps colds at bay and is reported to contain 20% more vitamin C than oranges. Many people have also shared stories of being paid as children to pick rosehips for Delrosa. The collected fruits would be taken in to school, weighed and the child would be paid according to the weight of the rosehips collected. Child labour? Surely not!

There were quite a few "off the shelf" tonics available to us in the early twentieth century. Scott's Emulsion, Parrish's Chemical Food and Fennings' Fever Cure - to name but a few.

All are remembered with varying degrees of revulsion.

Scott's Emulsion was almost the same consistency as paint. Rich in cod liver oil, it was guaranteed to "build you up"!

Parrish's Chemical Food would, I feel, have been one of the few things to have benefitted from a sell by date being applied. I've been told it was red, pink, purple, brown and "the colour of Tizer". With such a variety, I can only conclude that someone's "chemical food" had been in the cupboard a little too long! Interesting to note that, because Parrish's was so rich in iron, it was often taken through a straw to avoid rotting the teeth.

Fennings' Fever Cure was perhaps somewhat misnamed as it was a remedy for many ails, not just a fever, and it was certainly widely used as a tonic. Don't forget to dilute! Eric told me that there were only two words to describe Fennings' Fever Cure – "Bloody awful"!

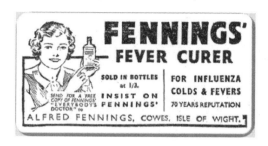

Dr Williams' Pink Pills for Pale People - a somewhat curiously titled tonic/remedy which came to us from across the Atlantic in the late 1890s. One can almost imagine the medicine man in his covered wagon travelling from settlement to settlement, plying his wares to the townsfolk and assuring them of the effectiveness of the little pills which had the capacity to improve wellbeing no matter what the cause of your suffering.

It occurs to me that there might in fact be a "P" missing when discussing Dr Williams' Pink Pills for Pale People - the missing "P" may well be placebo!

Keeping the "pink" theme going; Lydia Pinkham was also busy in 19th Century America producing her Vegetable Compound to cure a variety of ailments (mainly women's complaints and especially "female hysteria"!). Lydia's compound was the inspiration for the Scaffold's hit single "Lily the Pink". Seemingly Mrs Pinkham's compound was 40% alcohol

...probably the reason why it was so popular during the prohibition years in the USA!

A hot toddy or a tot of whisky in your cuppa, either to start or end the day would be a much favoured tonic. As would the rather scary "raw eggs and sherry" - often called an egg flip. Boxers favoured the egg flip as a pre-match tonic but so did ordinary working folk. Nursing mothers and older ladies were very fond of the odd glass of stout. Whether you were drinking Guinness or Mackieson, everyone would have plunged the poker in to the stout before drinking it. Why? Numerous reasons have been offered, amongst them - "to take the chill off it", "to stop it fizzing"? However, the most likely reason takes us back to the charcoal and the remedies for a healthy digestive system.

Comfrey was one of the herbs most used for medicinal purposes. The leaves would frequently be used to soothe bumps, bruises and burns but would also be used to make a tonic tea. Modern herbalists warn against ingesting too much comfrey but in days gone by it would have been a regular tonic. Slippery elm might also have been taken as a tonic.

Some, most famously the actress Sarah Miles, would advocate drinking your own urine as a great tonic. You could also try washing in it to salve any skin problems.

However, no reflection on tonics and toddies would be complete without a quick chat about "keeping yourself regular"!

The number one laxative is, and it seems always has been, syrup of figs. But when given it's somewhat imperious title of "California Syrup of Figs" - it takes on the warmth and sunshine of that American state and makes everyone feel better about being "dosed up".

Cascara, bicarb, castor oil, cabbage water and rhubarb would have been amongst the most popular doses to flush you out!

Sennapods, sennacot and senna tea were high on the list of constipation remedies. Chewing liquorice root was another top cure. The fruity remedy we all loved to hate were prunes. Interesting to note that when school dinners were introduced, prunes were to be found on the menu every week! And nearly always on the same day of the week...Friday. One of my reminiscers fondly recalled that prunes were known as "black coated workers" in her family!

Soap would work a treat on the those lazy bowels...simply insert a small piece of unscented soap in to the bottom and wait for it to work it's mysterious magic.

Liquid paraffin might be used to relax the bowels. Although when I visited Cheshire I was told of a lady whose doctor prescribed liquid paraffin to aid her constipation problems. This lady felt that to use the liquid paraffin for this purpose would be a terrible waste and instead used it to make some very delicious pastry.

I've also been advised that you shouldn't bother with any lotions or potions to loosen your bowels; instead you should just listen to a terrifying ghost story!

Children were dosed up once a week and, no matter where I have travelled, it would be true to say that it was always the same night of the week...Friday. Friday night meant no school, church or Sunday school the next day so you could stay close to home and wait for the potions to do their trick. I often reflect on my visit to a packed Methodist Central Hall when a gentleman who had been quiet throughout the session, folded his arms and threw his head back before announcing loudly to the assembled group that Friday night was in fact "clearing out night"! All the evidence would suggest that he was correct in his summation.

Of course those trips to the lavatory would have been concluded with ceremonious wiping with newspaper. Fond recollections of newspaper threaded on string hanging on the back of the door of the outside loo. The more classy folk of south Cheshire said they were quite fond of cutting their newspaper up with pinking shears... it makes my eyes water just thinking about that!

Much good advice would often be shared under the umbrella of prevention being better than cure. For example, you really don't want to sit on cold pavements and risk getting chincough (piles to you and me!).

On the somewhat delicate subject of birth control, I was advised by a very sweet and demure 94 year old that the best advice she could offer was to

"Keep your legs crossed!"

It should be noted that a knot in your nightie or a sixpence between your knees will be equally effective!

Advice may also have been sought from one of the various "medical ancillaries" to be found in every street. She was the lady in every community who took on the lead role whenever there was hatching or dispatching to be seen to. There are some glorious tales of these good natured ladies who would happily be interrupted whilst cooking the family tea to go and deliver a baby or lay out a body... quite often still wearing the same pinny!

We must not forget the revered and reviled "Nitty Nora", the school nurse – whether she was doling out the cod liver oil or checking for infestations, Nora was never the person school children wanted to see!

Many of grandma's cures are tried and true. Others have been tried and abandoned. Recently, scientists have made an important discovery regarding avoiding winter colds – have a good laugh! Researchers at Pennsylvania University found that happy people are three times less likely to succumb to a cold.

So this winter, strap some bacon to your chest, a mouse skin to your throat and eat a spoonful of woodlice. It won't stop you getting a cold, but the comedy value will make the rest of your family feel so much better and...

Laughter is by far the best medicine!

Acknowledgements

I owe a huge debt of gratitude to my husband Kevin who has accompanied me to so many reminiscence sessions...especially on dark winter evenings in remote rural locations. He has been a constant and patient support and encouragement in putting together this collection. Thank you so much!

Thanks too to Lesley Jones and Heather Jones for being my sounding boards and proof readers.

I have already acknowledged the wonderful folk who have so freely shared their stories with me but I really am very grateful to you all for your generosity, enthusiasm and joining in with the spirit of reminiscence. Some names have been changed to prevent embarrassment!

Bibliography

Age Exchange - Can we afford the doctor? Age Exchange 1985

Culpeper, Nicholas - Culpeper's Complete Herbal. Wordsworth Reference 2007. ISBN 9781853263453

Chappell, Cherry - Grandma's Remedies. Random House 2009. ISBN 9781905211173

Root-Bernstein, Robert and Michele - Honey Mud Maggots. Macmillan 1999.ISBN 0333750381

Talks and Reminiscence Sessions

Since the early 1990's, I have been delivering talks and reminiscence sessions on a wide variety of changing themes. Most sessions have an accompanying PowerPoint presentation and all have a range of supporting books and resources. The following lists outline my current offers:

Talks

Suitable for larger group sessions - of particular interest to older age groups.

Dollytubs and Flat Irons - Interactive reminiscence session on the theme of doing the washing. Take a step back in time and recall the sweat (and tears) of washdays in the early-mid 20th Century.

Famous Folk of Staffordshire - A celebration of the most inspirational Staffordshire folks; from Philip Astley and his circus to Shane Meadows and his films - enjoy a whistle-stop trip around this great county.

Famous Folk of Stoke – A celebration of the great sons and daughters of the Stoke-on-Trent area and the contributions they have made to local, regional, national and international history. We will look at the famous potters, entertainers, sports stars and those folk who intrigue and inspire us.

Food Glorious Food - An interactive PowerPoint presentation looking at the advent, and impact, of convenience foods in our diet. From fish fingers to angel delight, Camp coffee to Chianti in a basket, spam to salmon paste - all the things we have loved... and some of those we have hated!

Goose Grease and Brown Paper - Can we afford the doctor? Of course not! A fun trip down memory lane to pre-NHS days and the kitchen cupboard remedies inflicted by our nearest and dearest! Honey, salt, onions, mustard...not to forget the snails, urine, string and cow muck!

Gymslips and Chalkboards- An interactive schooldays reminiscence session recalling the highlights of the "best days of our lives" - uniforms, books and poems, times tables, inkwells...and playtime!

Make Do and Mend - Recycling was always a way of life...share your top tips and recipes. Reminisce about eating chitterlings, pigs' trotters, tripe...and for afters...a deluxe vanilla slice! Don't forget to save a bit of beetroot to touch up your lipstick.

'Tis the Season to be Jolly...- Christmas time! A look back at some of our Christmas traditions, celebrations and favourite toys! Enjoy a few carols and a look at the films we've watched at Christmas time.

To Love and to Cherish - A celebration of our wedding traditions and superstitions. A quick look at weddings dresses from the 40's through to the 70's and at some of the dresses and traditions of other faiths/cultures. A peek at some of the weddings of the rich and famous... including Lady Di's crumpled frock!

Watching with Mother - Children's TV Favourites from the 50's-70's. Remembering Muffin the Mule and Andy Pandy, listening to some of the classic theme tunes including Black Beauty and Blue Peter.
If it's Friday and it's five to five, then it must be....?

Reminiscence Sessions

Suitable for small groups in residential and mild dementia care settings.

- Dollytubs and Flat Irons

- Famous Folk of Stoke

- Food Glorious Food

- Goose Grease and Brown Paper

- Gymslips and Chalkboards

- Holidays and Outings

- Make Do and Mend

- On the Playground

- People's War

- Weddings

To purchase copies of this book, to enquire about talks and reminiscence sessions or to share an anecdote please contact Kath on:

Tel: 01538 722812

or

Email: kreyno9128@aol.com